It's early in Batman's career and the Dark Knight's war on crime is starting to go well. Criminals are beginning to fear the Batman and the police are starting to work with him. Of course, it's going so well because Batman hasn't met the Joker yet...

LEGENDS of the DARK KNIGHT

Images Part One

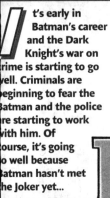

BATMAN
Bruce Wayne has only recently started his crusade and doesn't have a Robin yet.

THE JOKER
Failed stand-up? Psycho bank-robber? Crime boss Red Hood? Who knows?

JAMES GORDON
Captain in the Gotham City Police Department and friend of Batman.

HENRY HAIGHT
Millionaire banker and member of the upper class of Gotham society.

SO WE BEAT ON, BOATS AGAINST THE CURRENT, BORNE BACK CEASELESSLY INTO THE PAST.
-- F. SCOTT FITZGERALD

Batman created by BOB KANE.

Suggested by the work of BILL FINGER and BOB KANE.

A tale from the early days by—
DENNIS O'NEIL story
BRET BLEVINS art
DIGITAL CHAMELEON colors
WILLIE SCHUBERT letters
GOODWIN & KAPLAN editors

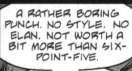

NICE MUFFIN... GOT A TREAT FOR YOU. LITTLE YUMMERS NUMMERS FOR YOUR MILK.

NOW WHERE'S THAT TAPE RECORDER...?

AH, HERE.

SHALL I GO FOR HUMOR OR STARK DRAMA?

I'M FEELING POETIC--

ATTENTION: TUESDAY NIGHT AT PRECISELY EIGHT, I'LL MAKE HENRY HAIGHT--

--THE LATE HENRY HAIGHT--

CATCH A LIFT, CAPTAIN?

OKAY, SERGEANT. GET IN.

HOW FAR YOU GOING, SERGEANT?

AS FAR AS IT TAKES--

EVERYTHING SET?

DOORS, WINDOWS AND VENTILATION DUCTS SEALED.

THE BOMB SQUAD TOOK EVERY PIECE OF FURNITURE APART AND USED DETECTORS ON THE FLOOR BOARDS.

"EVERY GUEST HAS BEEN IDENTIFIED BY AT LEAST TWO OF THE DINNER'S ORGANIZERS, AND THERE ARE TWENTY COPS SCATTERED AROUND THE ROOM. THE FOOD'S BEEN PREPARED BY--

--POLICE DEPARTMENT CHEFS, AND--

--ANYWAY, HAIGHT IS ON A DIET AND ISN'T EATING ANYTHING. YEAH, I KNOW.

I'VE PERSONALLY CHECKED THE MICRO-PHONE AND THE AREA AROUND THE PODIUM.

THERE'S NO WAY THIS JOKER CHARACTER CAN GET TO HAIGHT...

...AT LEAST NOT TONIGHT.

HEEEEEEEEEE

--DEAD BEFORE HE HIT THE FLOOR.

HENRY!

THE PAPER YOU'RE EXAMINING WAS THE MURDER WEAPON?

YES. HIS SPEECH. I SNAGGED IT IN MY HANDKERCHIEF WHILE EVERYONE WAS TENDING TO HENRY.

IT'S COATED WITH POISON... APPARENTLY ACTIVATED THROUGH BODY HEAT AND INTRODUCED INTO THE BLOOD THROUGH THE SKIN.

BUT WHAT POISON? IT'S NOTHING I'VE EVER SEEN...

...SOME STRANGE COMPOUND OF CHLORIDES AND HYDROCOLLOIDS WITH A PROTEIN CATALYST.

TO BE CONTINUED

PREVIOUSLY

When a meteor containing Superman's cousin, Supergirl, crashed to Earth, it littered the planet with Kryptonite. Since then different forms of Kryptonite have been regularly turning up on the Black Market from Metropolis to Gotham.

SUPERMAN
Kal-El's main weakness is from irradiated shards of his home planet.

LIVEWIRE
Former shock-jock radio DJ who now has the power to control electricity.

KRYPTONITE
Green Kryptonite weakens Superman, but different colours do different things.

FLASH
Wally West is the guardian of Keystone City and is also the Fastest Man Alive.

SUPERMAN BATMAN
K PART ONE:
STRANGE FAVOUR

GOTHAM TOWERS

This is ridiculous.

This is hysterical.

I KNOW THAT LOOK.

THAT'S THE FACE YOU MAKE BEFORE YOU START SPILLING ALL YOUR SECRETS.

YOU NEVER COULD KEEP A SECRET.

THERE'S ONE SECRET I NEVER DID TELL YOU. OR ANYONE.

WHY I FIGHT CRIME...

He's faster than a bolt of lightning.

He can stop a missile with two fingers.

He can mold titanium between his molars like gum.

But there is **one** substance that can tear him apart from the inside out.

One substance that can kill **him**.

Darkness.
After any time with Clark I start to crave it.
We tend to spend our time together on **big** things. Planets that need saving. Whole dimensions that need righting.
Big **bright** things.
The streets are simpler. Small-time crooks pulling small-time crimes.
The kind of problem I got into this business to fix.
The kind I can solve by **hand.**
Sometimes they even cry.
A **blur** stops my fun in the middle.
He's had enough fun for the night.
I knew it couldn't last.

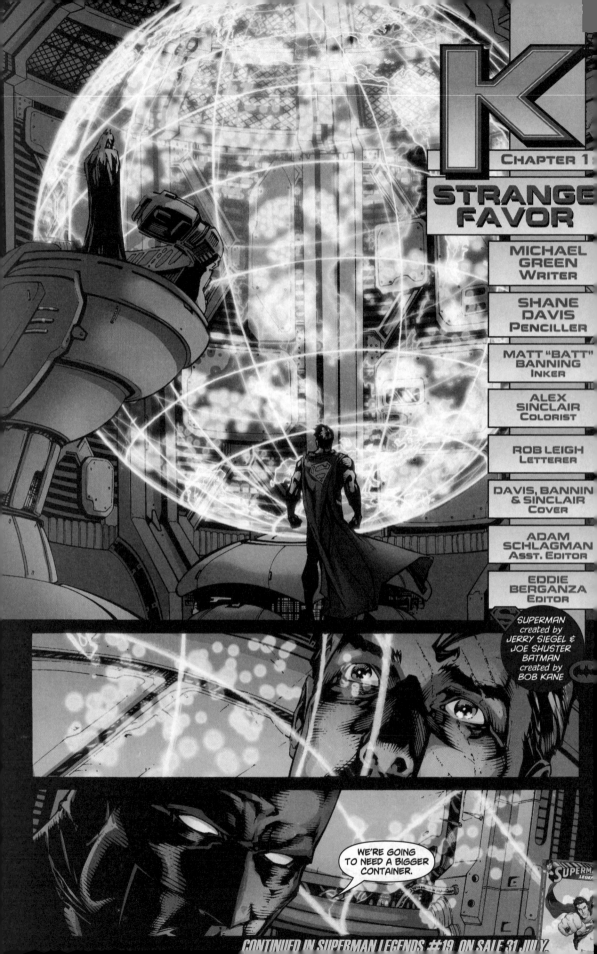

K

CHAPTER 1

STRANGE FAVOR

MICHAEL GREEN
Writer

SHANE DAVIS
Penciller

MATT "BATT" BANNING
Inker

ALEX SINCLAIR
Colorist

ROB LEIGH
Letterer

DAVIS, BANNIN & SINCLAIR
Cover

ADAM SCHLAGMAN
Asst. Editor

EDDIE BERGANZA
Editor

SUPERMAN
created by
JERRY SIEGEL &
JOE SHUSTER
BATMAN
created by
BOB KANE

WE'RE GOING TO NEED A BIGGER CONTAINER.

CONTINUED IN SUPERMAN LEGENDS #19. ON SALE 31 JULY.

ROLL CALL

I WALKED ALL THE WAY FROM *HELL*.

WITH A *SECRET* TO TELL.

ABOUT *BATMAN* AND ME.

space medicine

Grant Morrison Writer · Tony Daniel Penciller
Daniel, Florea, Glapion & Irwin Inkers
Guy Major Colorist · Randy Gentile Letterer ·
Jeanine Schaefer Assoc. Editor · Mike Marts Editor
batman · created by · bob kane

...YOU GOT MY ATTENTION.
NOW PUT THE WEAPON DOWN AND TELL ME WHAT IT IS YOU...
DDT!
UTT!
NOBODY MOVE OR HE'S DEAD!
THIS ONE'S BETWEEN ME AND HIM...AND THE BATMAN.
ASK FARELLI, ASK VANE.

ALL YOUR FAULT!

Ears ringing.

Arm's numb.

Can't seem to breathe.

Get up.

I WAS A GOOD OFFICER.

THIS POLICE DEPARTMENT... THIS CITY *BETRAYED* ME...

...SENT ME TO *HELL* TO LEARN FROM THE *DEVIL*.

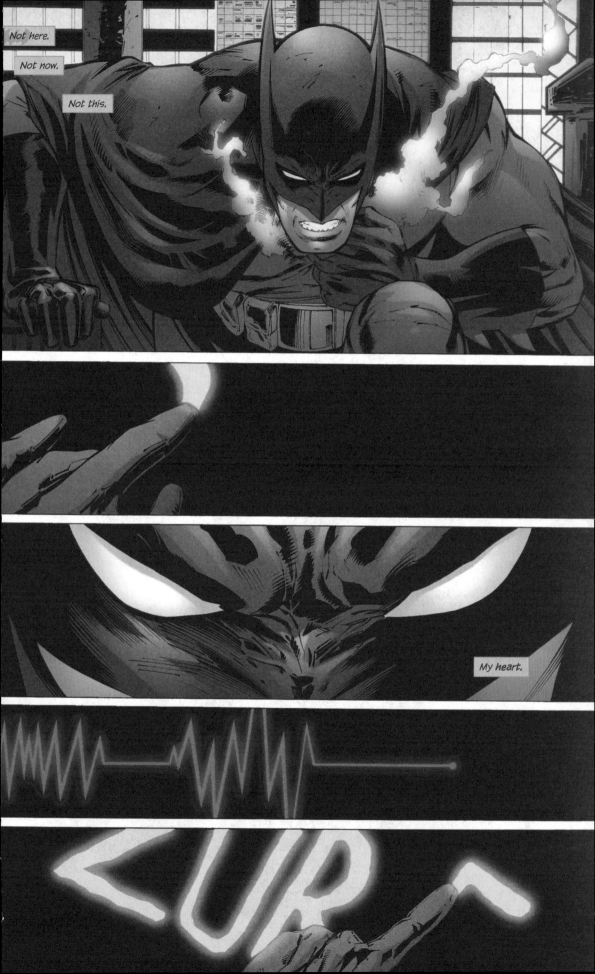

BRAIN DEATH OCCURS *FIVE MINUTES* AFTER *CARDIAC ARREST.*

A LOT CAN *HAPPEN* IN FIVE MINUTES.

ZUR EN ARRH

Uh oh...

...NOW YOU'VE DONE IT...

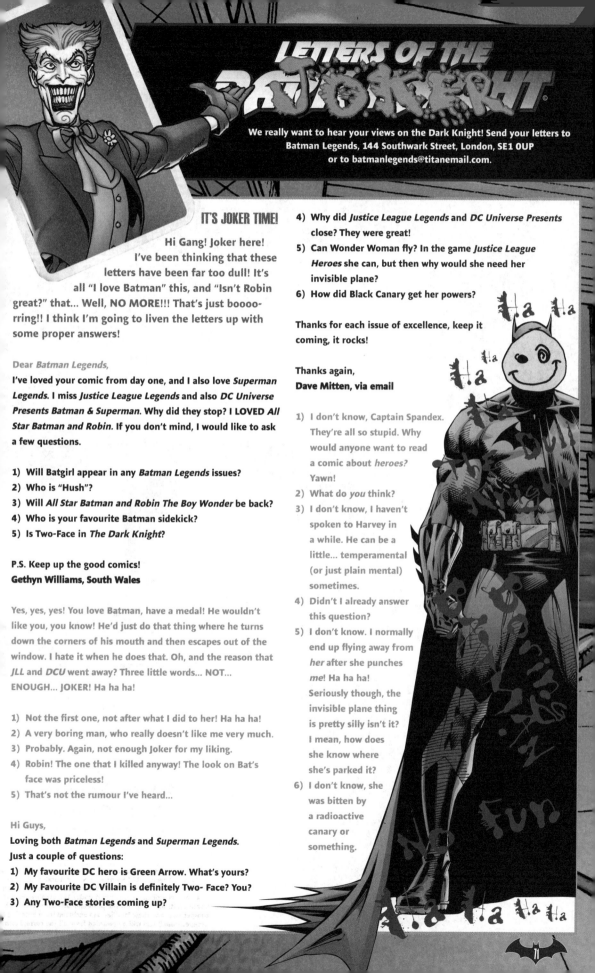

LETTERS OF THE DARK JOKER NIGHT

We really want to hear your views on the Dark Knight! Send your letters to Batman Legends, 144 Southwark Street, London, SE1 0UP or to batmanlegends@titanemail.com.

IT'S JOKER TIME!

Hi Gang! Joker here! I've been thinking that these letters have been far too dull! It's all "I love Batman" this, and "Isn't Robin great?" that... Well, NO MORE!!! That's just booooo-rring!! I think I'm going to liven the letters up with some proper answers!

Dear *Batman Legends*,

I've loved your comic from day one, and I also love *Superman Legends*. I miss *Justice League Legends* and also *DC Universe Presents Batman & Superman*. Why did they stop? I LOVED *All Star Batman and Robin*. If you don't mind, I would like to ask a few questions.

1) Will Batgirl appear in any *Batman Legends* issues?
2) Who is "Hush"?
3) Will *All Star Batman and Robin The Boy Wonder* be back?
4) Who is your favourite Batman sidekick?
5) Is Two-Face in *The Dark Knight*?

P.S. Keep up the good comics!
Gethyn Williams, South Wales

Yes, yes, yes! You love Batman, have a medal! He wouldn't like you, you know! He'd just do that thing where he turns down the corners of his mouth and then escapes out of the window. I hate it when he does that. Oh, and the reason that *JLL* and *DCU* went away? Three little words... NOT... ENOUGH... JOKER! Ha ha ha!

1) Not the first one, not after what I did to her! Ha ha ha!
2) A very boring man, who really doesn't like me very much.
3) Probably. Again, not enough Joker for my liking.
4) Robin! The one that I killed anyway! The look on Bat's face was priceless!
5) That's not the rumour I've heard...

Hi Guys,

Loving both *Batman Legends* and *Superman Legends*. Just a couple of questions:
1) My favourite DC hero is Green Arrow. What's yours?
2) My Favourite DC Villain is definitely Two- Face? You?
3) Any Two-Face stories coming up?

4) Why did *Justice League Legends* and *DC Universe Presents* close? They were great!
5) Can Wonder Woman fly? In the game *Justice League Heroes* she can, but then why would she need her invisible plane?
6) How did Black Canary get her powers?

Thanks for each issue of excellence, keep it coming, it rocks!

Thanks again,
Dave Mitten, via email

1) I don't know, Captain Spandex. They're all so stupid. Why would anyone want to read a comic about *heroes*? Yawn!
2) What do *you* think?
3) I don't know, I haven't spoken to Harvey in a while. He can be a little... temperamental (or just plain mental) sometimes.
4) Didn't I already answer this question?
5) I don't know. I normally end up flying away from *her* after she punches *me*! Ha ha ha! Seriously though, the invisible plane thing is pretty silly isn't it? I mean, how does she know where she's parked it?
6) I don't know, she was bitten by a radioactive canary or something.

BATMAN
GOTHAM KNIGHT

Batman Gotham Knight is a fresh and exciting new entry into the *Batman* mythos, spinning out of a 40-year history in animation including the Emmy® award winning *Batman: The Animated Series*, widely considered a pivotal moment in American animation.

Six standalone chapters, each with stylish art from some of Japan's greatest anime visionaires, weave together into a larger story that follows *Batman* through his transition from beginner to *The Dark Knight*.

COMPETITION...COMPETITION...COMPETITION...COMPETITIO

We've got ten copies of *Batman Gotham Knight* on DVD to give away!
To win a copy, just answer the following question:

Email the answer to
batmanlegends@titanemail.com

WHAT WERE THE NAMES OF BRUCE WAYNE'S PARENTS?

THE DARK KNIGHT

Batman (CHRISTIAN BALE) raises the stakes in his war on crime in Christopher Nolan's *The Dark Knight*. With the help of *Lieutenant Jim Gordon* (GARY OLDMAN) and District Attorney *Harvey Dent*, *Batman* sets out to dismantle the remaining criminal organizations that plague the city streets.

The partnership proves to be effective, but they soon find themselves prey to a reign of chaos unleashed by a rising criminal mastermind known to the terrified citizens of Gotham as *The Joker* (HEATH LEDGER.)

COMPLETE YOUR COLLECTION...

Batman Legends — Also Available # 1-15

 #16
 #17
 #18
 #19
 #20
 #21

Superman Legends — Also Available Issues # 1-10

 #11
 #12
 #13
 #14
 #15
 #16

Justice League Legends — Also Available Issue #1-3

 #4
 #5
 #6
 #7
 #8
 #9

DC Universe Presents

 #1
 #2
 #3
 #4
 #5
 #6

To order your Back Issues visit
www.titanmagazines.co.uk or Call ☎ 0844 844 0248

UK £3.00 EIRE £4.20*